MY ALPHABET
STICKER ACTIVITY BOOK

Use your pens, pencils and stickers to
complete the activities on each page.
Where there is a sticker missing,
you will see a silhouette like this:

Then press out the cards at the
back of the book, and use them
for playing pairs or snap. Have fun!

make
believe
ideas

Aa

Find the missing stickers, **and** then follow the lines to see which **animal** gets the **apples**.

adder

antelope

How many **ants** can you count?

....

Colour the **ape**.

apples

B b

Billy is having a **birthday** party!
Colour the **balloons blue**.

bee

How many
butterflies can
you count?

....

bread

ball

bananas

basket

Sticker the **birthday** cake.

3

Cc

Trace the **cloud**.

Colour the **castle**.

cow

calf

Sticker the princess's **crown**.

4

Dd

Doodle and sticker **disguises** on the **dogs**.

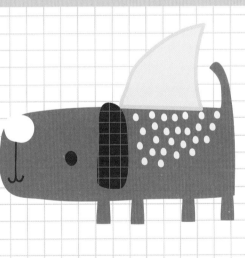

Use stickers to finish the pattern of **doughnuts**.

Ee

Sticker one more **eagle**.

eagles

How many **eggs** can you count?

....

Sticker **earmuffs** on the **emu**.

emu

Colour the **egg**.

Circle the pair of matching **exercising elephants**.

Draw pictures on the **easels**.

easels

Ff

Find the missing stickers, and then search the **farmyard** for the things on the list. Tick them off as you go.

fox ☐

flowers ☐

farmer ☐

frog ☐

Find and circle an animal that does not start with **f**.

Gg

Colour the **giant giraffe** in the **garden**.

giraffe

gate

grass

girl

Sticker **green glasses** and **gloves** on the **girl**.

9

Hh

Finish the scene with colour and stickers.

How many **hot-air balloons** can you count?

....

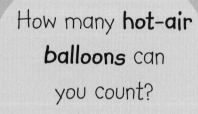

hot-air balloon

helicopter

Trace the **helicopter's** trail.

house

hill

11

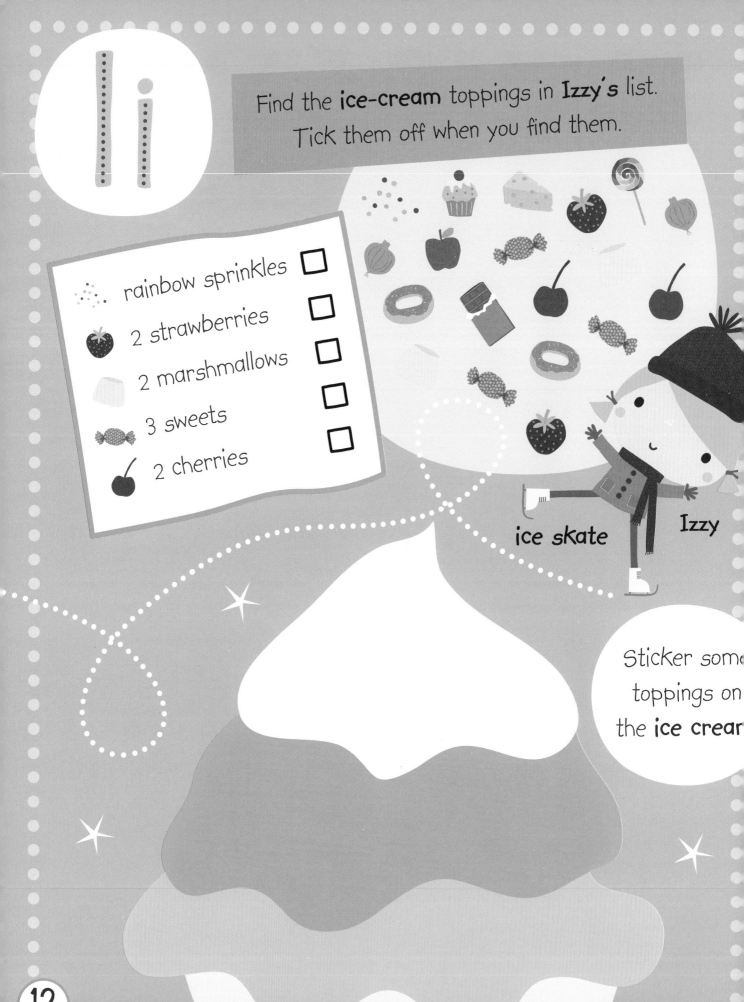

l i

Find the **ice-cream** toppings in **Izzy's** list.
Tick them off when you find them.

- rainbow sprinkles ☐
- 2 strawberries ☐
- 2 marshmallows ☐
- 3 sweets ☐
- 2 cherries ☐

ice skate

Izzy

Sticker some
toppings on
the **ice cream**

12

Jj

Help the **jaguars** count the **jewels**, and then sticker the answers to finish the sums.

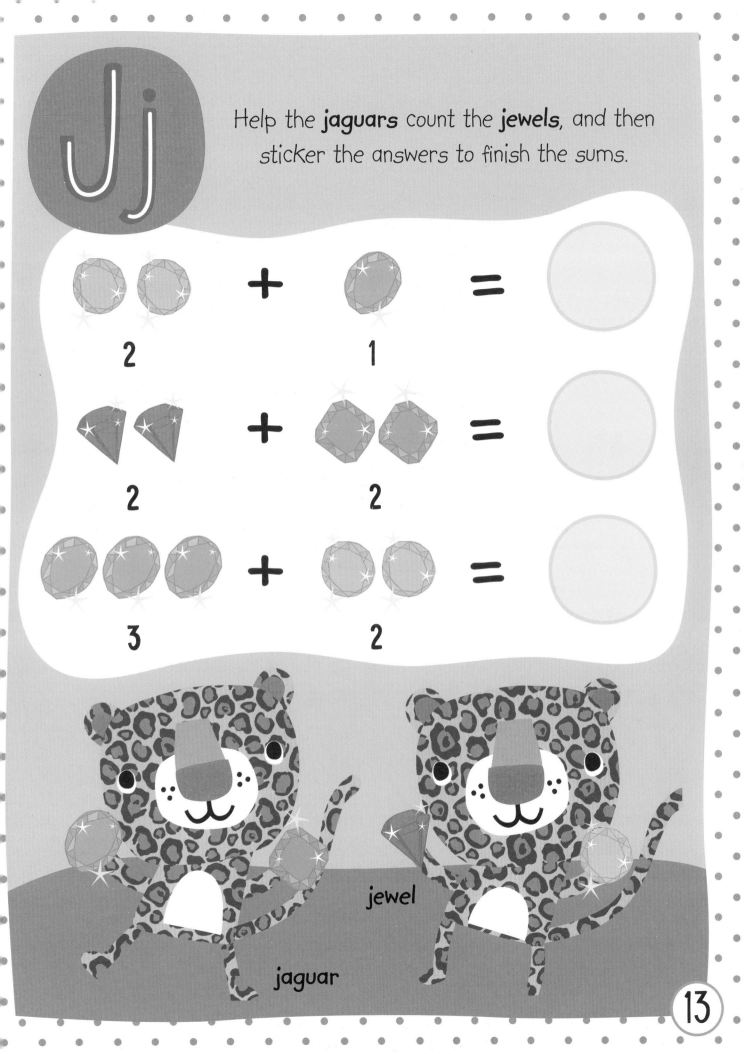

2 + 1 =

2 + 2 =

3 + 2 =

jewel

jaguar

13

Kk

The **koalas** are competing to **knit** the longest scarf!

Katie Koala

Kevin Koala

Kylie Koala

Draw a line from each **king** to the matching coloured **key**.

Sticker the winner's name on the trophy.

Ll

Follow the trails to see which **lifeboat**
will reach the **lighthouse**.

Lily

Luke

Lucy

light

Sticker the **lightning bolts**.

lighthouse

Mm

Copy the **mouse**. Use the grid to help you.

Circle five differences between the **monsters**.

marbles

16

Guide the **monkey** through the **maze** to reach his **mates**. Try to avoid the **mushrooms**!

How many **marbles** can you count?

....

Start

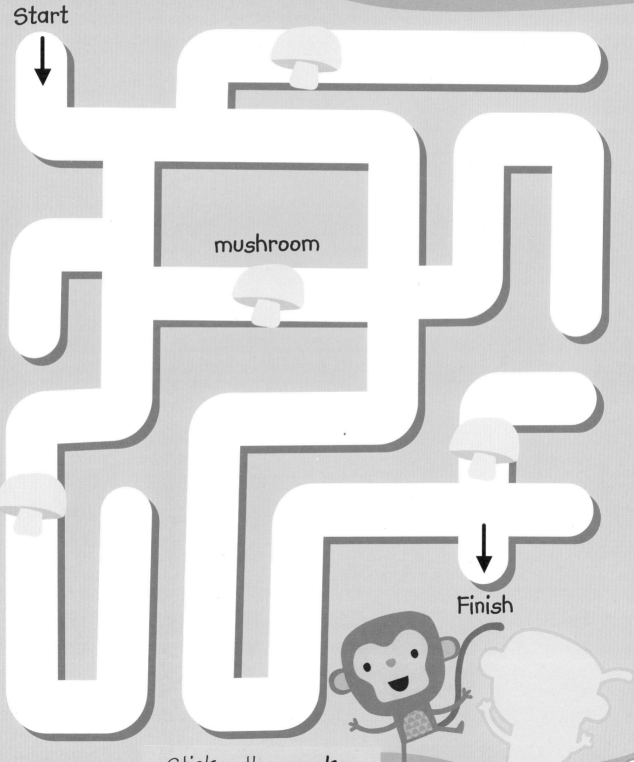

mushroom

Finish

Sticker the **monkey**.

Nn

Sticker another **newt** so there are **nine**.

Trace and then colour the **number nine**.

9

Colour **Nina** the **nurse**.

Oo

Find and circle an **owl** that looks exactly like this **one**.

Sticker an **onion** in **Ollie Otter's** oven.

1:00

19

Pp

Colour the **pair** of **pirates**.

Pete

Pat

Sticker the **portholes**. Who's inside the **pirate ship**?

pearls

parrot

Find the missing stickers to finish the **peacock painting**.

penguin

paintbrush

Circle the fruit that does not begin with **p**.

pear

pineapple

banana

peach

21

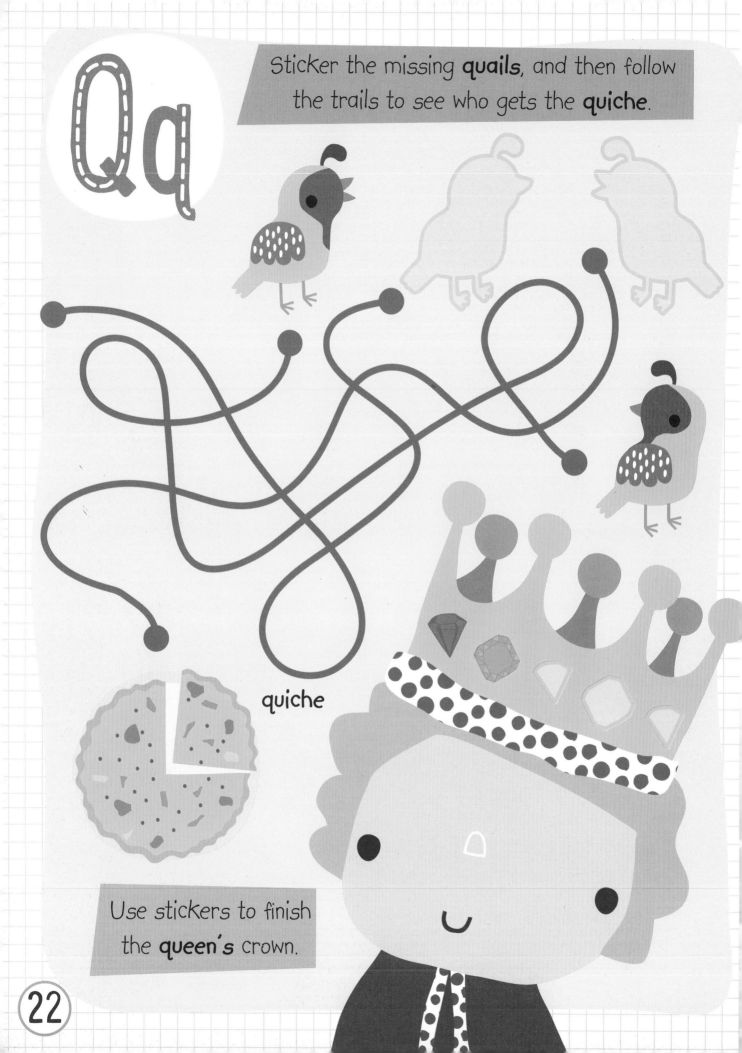

Qq

Sticker the missing **quails**, and then follow the trails to see who gets the **quiche**.

quiche

Use stickers to finish the **queen's** crown.

Rr

Use colour and stickers to finish the **rocket**.

How many **red** planets can you count?

....

23

Ss

Trace and then colour the **smiling sun**.

Decorate the **sandcastles** with **stickers**.

shell

sand

Circle the **starfish** that is different.

T t

Circle five differences between the **tennis-playing twins**.

How many **tomatoes** can you count?

....

Colour the **teddy bear**.

Uu

Use colour and stickers to finish the **underwater** scene.

How many **upside-down** things can you count?

....

26

Vv

Colour **Victor** the **vet**, and then help him with the tasks on his clipboard.

- Sticker a bandage on the hamster.

- Draw some tasty treats for the cat.

- Colour the turtle's shell.

VET

27

Ww

Trace the spider's **web**.

Sticker the objects in the correct **wheelbarrows**.

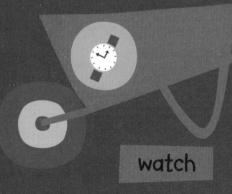

watch

wood

watermelon

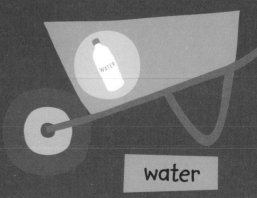

water

Sticker the
missing parts of
the **xylophone**.

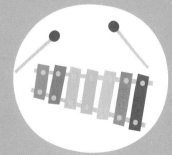

Yy

Sticker the missing **yo-yo** to finish the word.

T O

How many **yellow** things can you count?

....

 yak

yacht

yogurt

Z z

Colour and sticker animals at the **zoo**.

Trace the **zigzag** fence.

ALPHABET QUIZ

Find the missing stickers, and then circle the answers.

Who has a pie?

penguin

p

pige

Who has a blue balloon?

badger

beaver

book

balloon

bull

parrot

Which animal begins with c?

cat

giraffe

sheep

Which animal is eating chocolate?

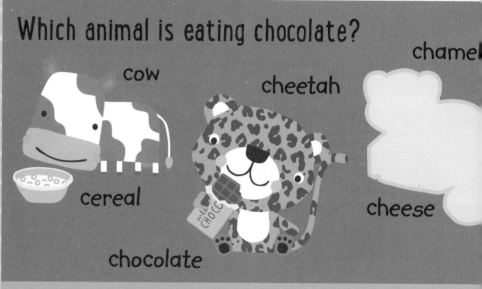

cow

cereal

cheetah

chocolate

cheese

chamel

Where is the lollipop?

lemon

lettuce

lollipo

32

PAIRS AND SNAP

Pairs (one or more players)

1) Press out the cards, and put them picture-side down on a table.
2) Take turns turning over two cards. If the cards match, put them aside. If they do not match, return them picture-side down to the table.
3) Keep going until you have found all the pairs. The player with the most pairs at the end is the winner!

Snap (two or more players)

1) Divide the cards equally between the players, picture-side down.
2) Take turns turning over a card and putting it on the table.
3) If a card matches the card beneath it on the pile, players call out, "Snap!" The first player to shout picks up all the cards on the pile.
4) When players have no cards left, they are out of the game.
5) Keep going until only one player is holding cards – this person is the winner!

cat

rocket

drum

penguin

ballerina

sun

farmer

peacock

rainbow

cake

house

cat

 frog

 pig

 rocket

 peacock

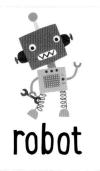 robot

 sun

 drum

 socks

 grapes

 rainbow

 ballerina

 farmer

 pig

 frog

 cake

 house

 socks

 robot

 penguin

 grapes

Pages 10-11 (continued)

Pages 12-13

5

3

4

Pages 14-15

Kevin Koala

Pages 16-17

Pages 18-19

Pages 20-21

puppy

panda

pig

Pages 20-21 (continued)

Pages 22-23

Robbie Robot

Pages 26-27

Page 24

Pages 28-29

Pages 30-31

Page 32

Extra Stickers

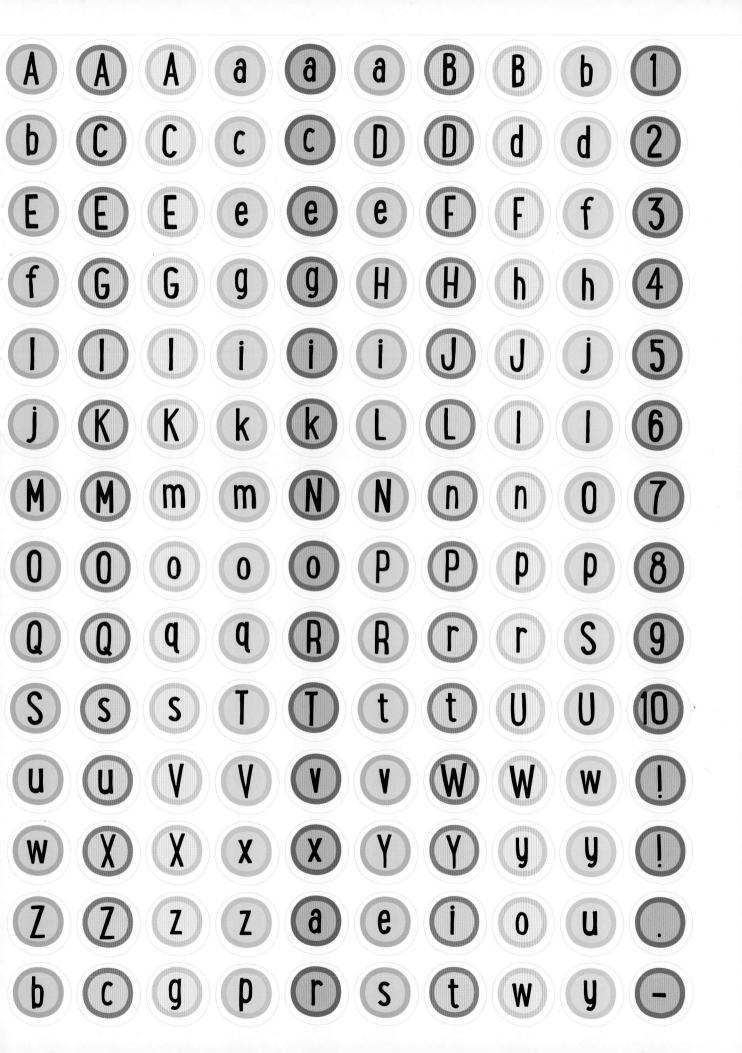